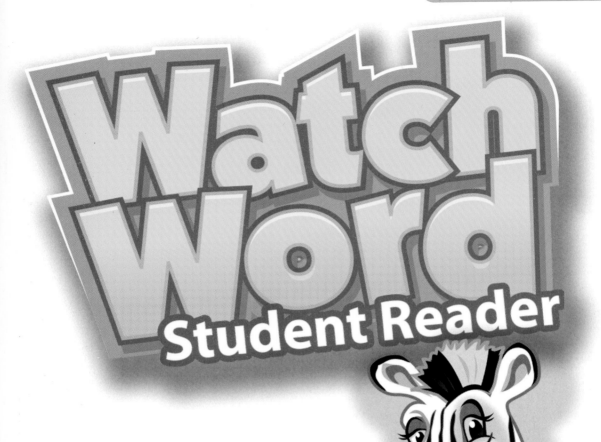

Watch Word
Student Reader

Stories by
Karen Lacey & Wendy Baird

Sopris West Educational Services
Longmont, CO

08 07 06   5 4 3 2

Edited by Karen Butler
Text layout by Kimberly Harris
Illustrations by Steve Clark
Cover design by Steve Clark

ISBN 1-59318-215-5

Printed in the United States of America

Published and Distributed by

SOPRIS
WEST
EDUCATIONAL SERVICES

4093 Specialty Place • Longmont, CO 80504 • (303) 651-2829
www.sopriswest.com

181READ/3-04/BAN/15M/039

Contents

Sam

Sam has a cat.

The cat is Mac.

Sam has a cap.

Mac sat on the cap.

Sam did pat the cap.
*

The cap is OK!

*

*Indicates word that has not been introduced. Students may require teacher assistance to read this word.

The Nap

Tom is a tot.

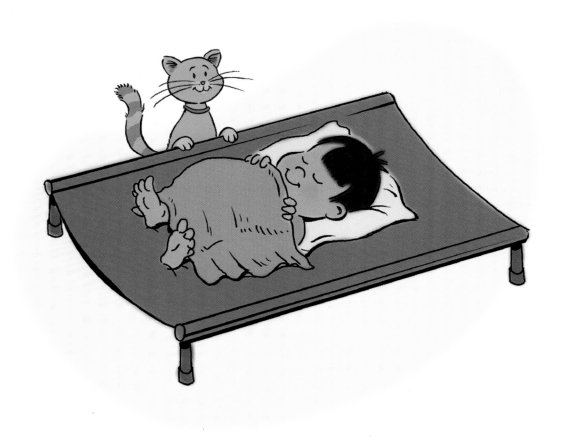

The tot can nap on a cot.

The cat is Sam.

Sam can nap on a cot.

The tot cannot nap on Sam.

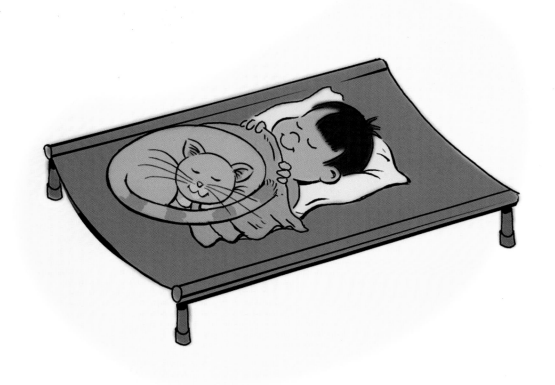

Sam can nap on top!

Todd

Todd is a pig.

Todd can dig and dig.

Todd did dig in the pot.

Todd did tip the pot.

"No, no, Todd!"

Todd did sit, but not in the pot.

Fun in the Sun

The sun is up.

Kim can run in the sun.

The sun is hot!

Kim is hot!

Kim has on a hat.

Now she can run in the sun!
*

*Indicates word that has not been introduced. Students may require teacher assistance to read this word.

The Egg

Meg is a big hen.

Meg has an egg.

Is the egg big?

The egg is not big.